Viola
Specimen Sight-Reading Tests

ABRSM Grades 1–5

from 2012

Notes

1 In the exam, candidates will be given a short interval
  of up to half a minute in which to look through and,
  if they wish, try out any part of the test before they
  are required to perform it for assessment.

2 The fingerings given in this book (as well as in the
  exam tests) are for guidance only. Examiners will not
  assess whether the given fingerings are observed.

Published by ABRSM (Publishing) Ltd, a wholly owned subsidiary of ABRSM
© 2011 by The Associated Board of the Royal Schools of Music
Music origination by Julia Bovee and Katie Johnston
Printed in England by Caligraving Ltd, Thetford, Norfolk,
on materials from sustainable sources
Reprinted in 2018

GRADE 1

GRADE 1

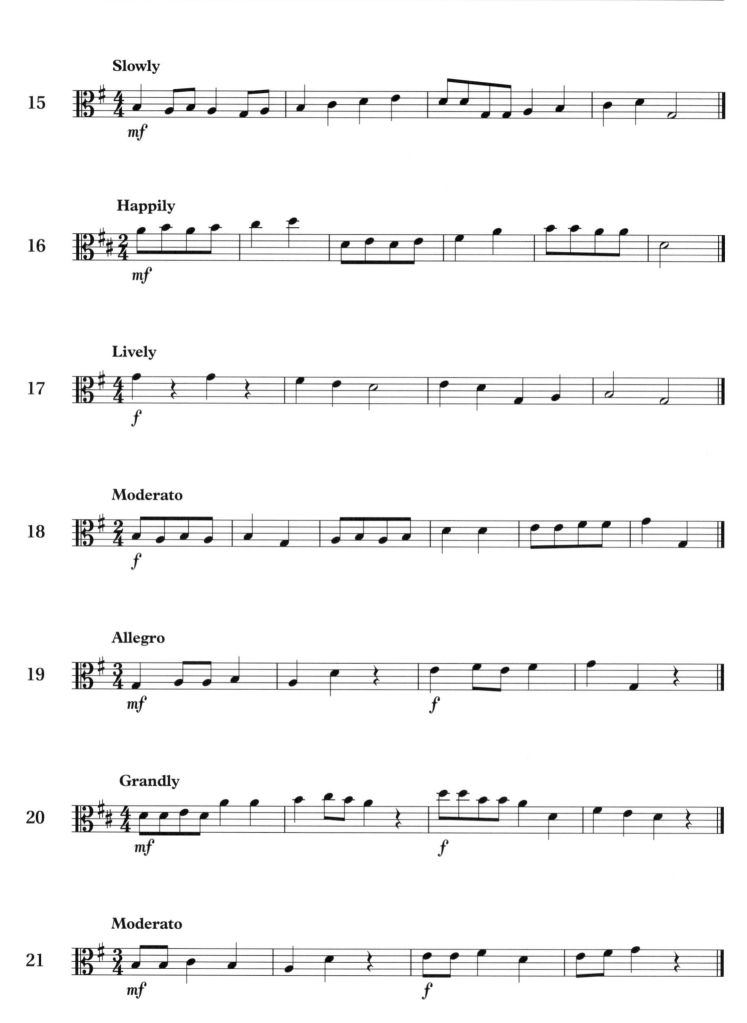

AB 3616

Andante

22

Allegro

23

Lively

24

Grandly

25

Gently

26

Moderato

27

Dancing

28

GRADE 2

AB 3616

GRADE 3

Risoluto

1

Playfully

2

Energico

3

Calmly

4

Expressively

5

Steadily

6

Giocoso

7

Andante

8

GRADE 3

21 **Energico**

22 **Lullaby**

23 **Andante**

24 **Allegretto**

GRADE 4

Andante grazioso

1

Hornpipe

2

Allegretto

3

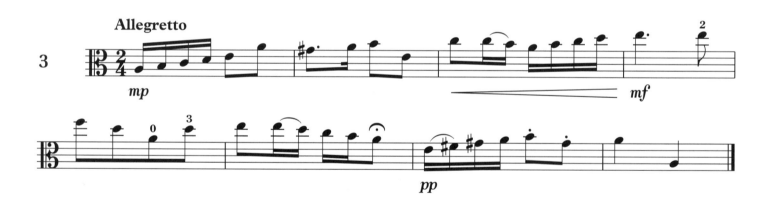

Leggiero

4

AB 3616

Allegro moderato

5

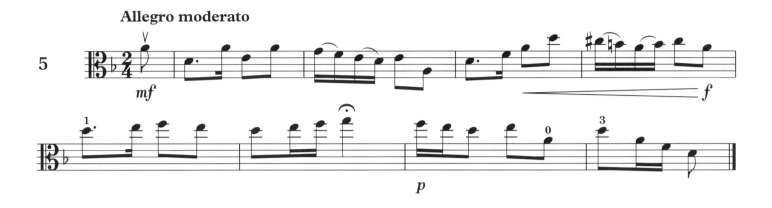

Tranquillo

6

Tempo di minuetto

7

Sostenuto

8

Grazioso

9

Allegretto leggiero

10

Animato

11

Giocoso

12
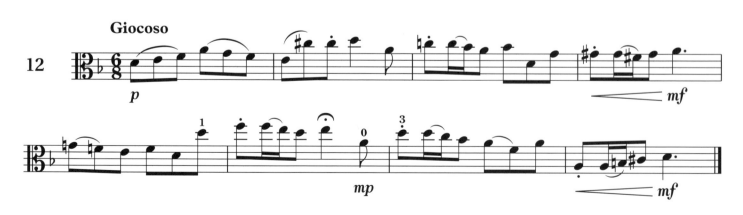

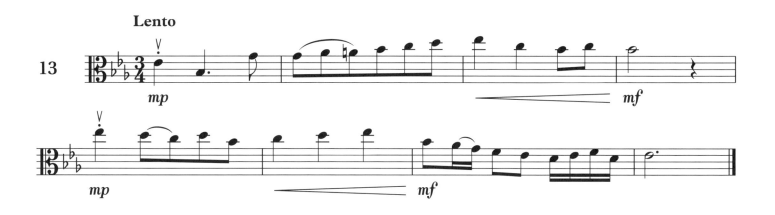

Cantabile

17

Agitato

18

Grandioso

19

Leggiero

20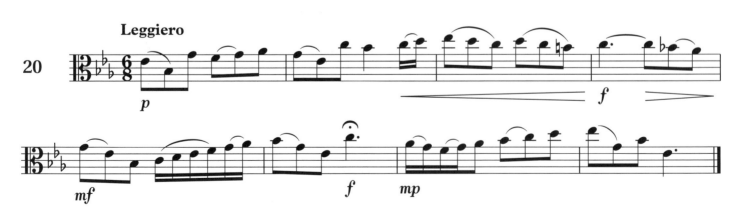

Dolce

21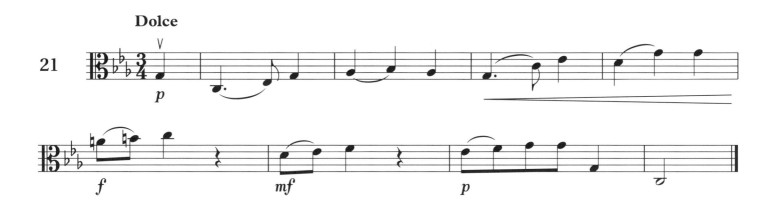

Grazioso

22

Andantino

23

Giocoso

24

1

Con brio

2

Allegro giocoso

3

Nobilmente

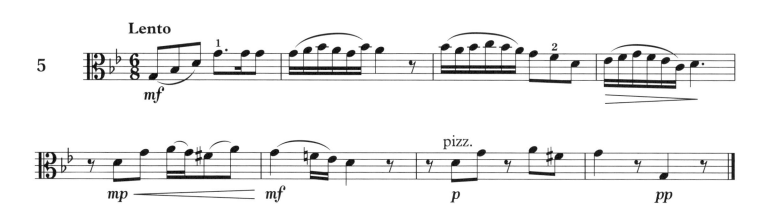

19

20

21